HORSE CENTS

Horse Cents

Mandi Summit

Red Quill Co LLC

This edition first printing, February 2023

Proofread by J. Nicole Starnes of Jot & Tittle: A Proofreading Service, LLC

Illustrated by Tracy Herrmann of Children Book Art by Tracy Ann

ISBN 979-8-9874781-1-0 (paperback)
ISBN 979-8-9874781-0-3 (eBook)

www.RedQuillCo.com

This book is dedicated to
my thoughtful ballerina, Ember Dawn,
and my adventurous cowgirl,
Karissa Brooke.

CONTENTS

One of the greatest gifts you can give your kids is to teach them to be responsible, empowered adults around money.

—Unknown

A LETTER FROM THE AUTHOR

Dear Parents,

Clover's story is based on my own personal childhood lesson in saving money. I remember very clearly laying my eyes upon a giant stuffed Simba from *The Lion King* in a Toys"R"Us store. In that moment, I wanted nothing more than that stuffed animal. I had my allowance in hand but it wasn't anywhere near enough to get what I really wanted. After begging and pleading with my parents to pay the difference, they insisted it was time that I learned to save my money.

Just as Clover's dad promises to take her back to the store as soon as she saves up enough money, my parents made the same promise to me. Soon after, I opened my first savings account at my local bank and learned the value of saving. When I eventually returned to buy that stuffed Simba, it was on sale! My patience had truly paid off and I've been successfully balancing the occasional splurge with frugality ever since.

With my first daughter on the way in 2016, this core memory, a background in banking, and a lifelong love of horses all worked together to kindle the inspiration for this book. I began working on a children's chapter book that would eventually become *Horse Cents*. After writing the first draft, I set it down and forgot all about it as I was swept away into the busyness of motherhood.

Finally, in late 2022, I happened upon the saved file on my computer titled *Horse Cents*, and my desire to get it published was reignited. Now a passionate editor with connections in the book publishing world, I decided it was time for me to stop procrastinating and dip my toes in the waters of being a published author.

My goal with *Horse Cents* is to help teach kids about the value of patience and saving their money. Because of this, I have chosen as a stylistic choice to have all dollar amounts written in numerical form to emphasize them for my young readers.

I've added some discussion questions at the end of the book in case you want to use them to guide a conversation about saving money and opening a bank account with your child. To assist even further, I have also included a glossary of banking terms for those young minds who want to build a deeper understanding of the banking world.

As a bonus, there is a second glossary of horse-related terms for any aspiring equestrians out there who share my love of horses.

Thank you for purchasing a copy of *Horse Cents!* I truly hope you enjoy reading about Clover's adventures with saving her money as much as I enjoyed writing about it. Please remember to leave me an honest review wherever you purchased this book and spread the word.

Happy trails,
Mandi Summit

Clover is based on my Morgan horse, Kaylee. She is
pictured here with her best friend, Blue, my mini paint horse.

1

ALLOWANCE DAY

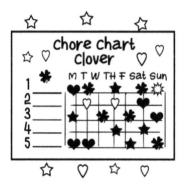

Clover's eyes fluttered open as the sun trickled through her window onto the quilt she was snuggled under. She yawned sleepily and stretched her legs out before remembering what day it was. It was allowance day!

Every week, Clover had a list of chores to take care of. Some chores she only had to do once a week, like sweeping the barn floor. Other chores were supposed to be done every day, like putting her toys away after she was done playing with them and setting the table for dinner.

Whenever she completed a chore, she got to put a shiny star sticker on the chore chart to mark it as complete. She was pretty good about doing her chores done because she liked the reward she received at the end of each week. If she got all her chores marked with stars by the time Saturday rolled around, she would get a whole $10 for her allowance! The best part was that Clover got to spend that money however she wanted, just like a grown-up.

Sometimes Mom or Dad would need help with something, and that would count as a bonus star that she could trade in for something special. She could choose between a sweet treat, like a molasses-dipped apple, or a fun family activity, like a game night where she got to choose the game.

She could also choose to save up her bonus stars for a while and earn something extra special—a family adventure! A trail adventure near the lake took two bonus stars, a dinner out at a restaurant took four, or she could even save up enough to go to the Cross-Country Jumps Theme Park!

But Clover wasn't known for her patience. So far, she had not been able to save her bonus stars up for any big family adventures because the things she could enjoy right now were simply more tempting. Why would she want to wait when she could have something special right now?

Heart pounding with excitement, Clover leapt out of bed and ran to the bathroom to brush her teeth and comb her mane. After she finished, she searched through the barn for Mom, at last finding her outside in the garden. Mom dropped the bunch of carrots she'd been picking into her basket and smiled at Clover.

"Good morning, sweetie!"

"Morning, Mom," Clover greeted her with excitement. "It's Saturday! Can I have my allowance, please?"

2

A LONG WAIT

"Good job this week, Clover," Mom said after they'd walked back inside the barn and checked the chore chart.

Mom dug in the allowance jar with her lips and got ahold of a $10 bill. Passing it to her daughter, she said,

"You did all of your weekly chores, so you earned your $10 allowance."

"Yay!" Clover took the money, excitement lighting up her big brown eyes. "Thank you, Mom!"

"Wait," Mom said as Clover turned to leave. "You also earned a bonus star this week for helping me cook dinner last night. Do you want to save it or spend it?"

Clover thought Mom must be joking. Of course, she wanted to spend it!

Putting her newly earned star right back into the star bank, she asked, "Can I have some peppermints, please?"

Mom laughed and got a bowl down to fill with a few peppermint candies.

"Oh, Clover . . . being patient isn't always a bad thing, you know."

"I know. I just don't want to be patient right now." She took the bowl from Mom and sat down. "Can you take me to the store after I eat my peppermints?"

"I'm afraid I can't today, sweetie. I've got a lot to get done before winter begins. But I'm sure Dad would be happy to when he's done working in the field."

Clover glanced at the clock. It wasn't even lunchtime. Dad wouldn't be home for five more hours! She groaned in frustration.

"What am I supposed to do until then?" she complained.

"Well, you could help me pick carrots, or you could go run a few laps in the arena, or—"

"Thanks, Mom," Clover interrupted, "but I'll figure something out." She was trying to be nice, but those ideas didn't sound fun at all.

Mom smiled and went back out to the garden.

Alone in the kitchen, Clover munched on her peppermints and began wondering about the things she could buy from the store later with Dad. She could get new ribbons for her mane, a brush to keep her coat all smooth and shiny, or some glitter paint to decorate her palomino coat for the upcoming parade.

She looked at the clock again.

"It's only been ten minutes?" she complained to herself.

Clover felt frustrated. Mom always told her that patience was a good skill to have, but Clover found waiting to be a difficult thing to do.

3

I WANT IT NOW

Clover's excitement kept growing with the possibilities all day long. She tried several things to distract herself from the long wait. She colored for a while, checked in with Mom a few times, ran around the arena, practiced her rearing, and when five o'clock finally grew close, she stared at the door waiting for it to open.

At long last, Dad finished plowing the fields on their farm and trotted into the barn. Clover couldn't wait any longer. She wanted to go to her favorite store and spend her money *right now.*

"Daddy!" Clover exclaimed as she ran to meet him at the door. "I got my allowance today."

"You did?" Dad said, and then smiled. "You must have worked hard this week. You should be proud of yourself, sweetheart."

"I am!" Clover said, prancing in front of him. Then she asked the big question, "Will you please take me to Mane Attraction so I can buy something? Pretty please?"

Mom looked over from preparing the apples and carrots for their dinner. "What if you saved your allowance for something extra special? Maybe we should talk about opening up your very own savings account. Wouldn't that be exciting?"

Clover wrinkled her nose in disgust. Mom always tried to get her to save her bonus stars and allowance, but that seemed so boring. Why should she save her money when she could go to the store and get something fun and new today?

Mom laughed at her daughter's obvious displeasure. "I know it's tough being patient, sweetie, but you already have so many ribbons and glitter paint. Instead of getting things that you already have or little items that you'll quickly grow bored of, wouldn't you enjoy something extra special for once?"

"Like what?" Clover asked, doubtfully.

"I don't know, but I'm sure there's something you've been wishing to get that you couldn't afford with just $10. If you save up for a while, you could get it. A new saddle, maybe? A pretty blue halter? A new grooming bucket?"

Clover thought about it for a moment. Those things did sound nice . . .

Dad raised his eyebrows and added knowingly, "Some brand-new, sparkly horseshoes?"

He didn't need to remind her that she had been wanting some new horseshoes for a very long time— the shiny ones that glittered when they caught the sunlight and clip-clopped on the pavement. She'd heard they even came in colors now! Maybe she could get them in her favorite color, pink.

But then again, that would mean she wouldn't be able to have anything new right now. Clover would have to be patient and wait if she wanted the horseshoes. Probably for a long time too. She didn't remember how much the horseshoes were anyway, so how would she even know when she had enough to get them? And yes, she did have a lot of glitter paints and bows, but could you really have too much of a good thing?

Then again, Clover loved the idea of something more extravagant than glitter paint and bows for once.

She hadn't been able to afford things like that before. Maybe if she were patient and saved up, she would finally be able to get those sparkly horseshoes she wanted so badly.

"Hmm . . . maybe," Clover thought aloud. After a brief pause, she turned to Dad. "But could you just take me to the store to make sure, Daddy?"

Her parents both laughed, but Dad agreed to trot with her down to the store.

4

MANE ATTRACTION

As they neared the large barn, Clover's eyes read the store's big glowing sign: Mane Attraction. Everyone agreed that this store was by far the best around for getting all the fun and fancy things Clover loved so much. Mane Attraction had everything a horse of any age could ever want for work, play, parades, and more.

Clover felt her excitement peak as the door slid open at their approach. Entering the store, her eyes darted around the various departments and displays. They had brushes and hoof picks, fly masks and sprays, all kinds of treats and toys, winter blankets, shampoos and conditioners, halters and bridles, saddles and saddle blankets, and so much more.

The store always kept a "Just In" display near the front that had something new and exciting each time she came in. This time, it was a giant inflatable soccer ball, and Clover immediately pictured herself kicking it around the pasture at home. Searching for the price tag, she read, "Only $40!"

Her eyes dropped to the ground in disappointment. She only had $10. That wouldn't be enough for the soccer ball.

Noticing that Clover looked sad, Dad offered, "You could save your money like Mom suggested."

"Yeah, but that would take"—Clover did some quick math in her head—"three more weeks!" The idea of saving her money and returning home with empty saddlebags didn't sound very fun, and she let out a sigh of exasperation.

"That's true," Dad acknowledged. "Well, do you want to look around some more?"

Clover nodded, and they walked further into the store. Just then, she spotted a beautiful saddle with gorgeous detailed sunflower tooling. Her eyes widened with unbridled adoration, and she imagined herself cantering around the arena with it on her back. All her friends would tell her how wonderful it looked and admire the way the dark leather contrasted with her light fur.

She trotted over to the saddles and read the tag hanging off the sunflower-decorated saddle horn.

"$1,800!" she nearly shouted. Clover let out another huge sigh. She'd never be able to afford it—it would take her years to save up that much money.

Forget it, she thought to herself. Saving money would take too long. It was too frustrating to look at all the things she couldn't afford. She wanted something *now*, something she could take home and enjoy *today*.

5

THE HORSESHOES

"We still haven't looked at the horseshoes you've been wanting," Dad said.

Clover nodded in acknowledgment and turned away from the saddles. And that's when she saw them—sparkly horseshoes in a rainbow of colors! There was pink, blue, purple, yellow, teal, orange, red, and green.

She trotted over with Dad following closely behind. The sign hanging above them read, "New! Imprint Horseshoes: $15."

Clover flipped a few over with her nose and saw all sorts of imprint shapes on the bottoms: butterflies, mini horseshoes, hearts, stars, moons, clovers, and dragonflies. If she wore these, everywhere she trotted would leave imprints on the ground of whatever shape she chose. Clover's eyes sparkled with longing.

"Oh, Daddy! Look at those horseshoes. Aren't they pretty?"

"They are very nice, Clover. They cost $15 each, so four of them would be $60. How much money do you have?"

Clover's lower lip hung even lower and quivered with disappointment. "I only have $10," she whined.

"Hmm, $10 isn't enough for those horseshoes." Looking around, Dad said, "You could buy one of these." He nudged a box of plain silver horseshoes with his nose.

Clover scoffed. They weren't even shiny or anything!

"Of course," he continued, "for $10, you could only afford one right now."

"What good would one horseshoe do?" Clover's eyes began to tear up. "It's not even sparkly!"

"I know it's disappointing, Clover, but you could always do what Mom suggested and save up for the ones you really want," he said.

Clover thought for a moment. If she was really good about doing her chores and earned $10 every week, it would take her five more weeks of saving her allowance in order to buy four of the imprint horseshoes.

That's a very long time to be patient, she thought, looking around for something less expensive.

6

FEELING BLUE

Defeated, Clover turned toward a familiar section of the store and walked slowly toward it. She looked over the bottles of glitter paint. Pink? No, she had two bottles of pink at home. Purple? No. Blue? Green? Yellow? No, no, and no. Clover already had every color here.

She moved over to the bows. There weren't any new patterns since the last time she'd bought one. *Ugh!* Clover became more and more upset as the minutes ticked by. After seeing those horseshoes, nothing else looked nearly as exciting anymore.

"What's that?" Dad said, motioning with his nose to a new addition in Clover's most-visited aisle.

She followed his gaze and noticed the feather clips. They had some in every length and color! Some were natural, while others were dyed in bright colors. Each clip had one to three feathers attached at varying heights so they'd interweave into your mane. Some of them even had beads and extra lengths of ribbon dangling.

She closed her eyes and imagined them in her own mane as she tossed her head and shook her mane in the air. *Oh!* How pretty they would look while she pranced down the street in the parade! Hope rose within her once more as she searched for the sign that would tell her their price.

"Feather Clips: $10 and Up."

Her heart leapt in her chest. She could actually afford one of them! Clover looked at her favorite one, but it was marked $15. Her second favorite was the same price. When she finally found the ones that only cost $10, she noticed they were the simplest of all the designs—only one or two feathers, *boring* brown, and no beads. It didn't exactly make her leap for joy.

"If you wait one more week, you would have $20. Then you could get a fancy feather clip and you'd even have $5 left over," Dad hinted.

"Can't you just loan me $5 so I can get it now, Daddy?" Clover gave him her best pleading eyes, but her efforts were in vain.

Dad let out a chuckle, which upset Clover even more. She didn't find this situation very funny.

"I'm sorry, Clover, but I can't always bail you out or you'll never learn the importance of saving your money."

This was not what Clover wanted to hear. She cast her gaze down at the ground and Dad nuzzled her shoulder lovingly.

"Ah, Clover. I wish I could just buy you whatever you wanted right when you wanted it every single time, but that wouldn't teach you anything. When you have to be patient and work hard for something, you appreciate what you have so much more."

Clover didn't care for the lecture in the midst of her disappointment. It was clear Dad wasn't going to get a feather clip or the horseshoes for her, so they may as well leave the store. Being here was only making her more upset. She was even starting to feel angry.

"Fine, let's just go home then," she said.

"Clover . . ." Dad nudged her shoulder gently with his nose to get her attention. She looked up at him with watery eyes, and he continued in a gentle voice. "Sometimes the things we really want are just out of reach, like these feather clips or that soccer ball. Sometimes the things we *really* want take an even longer time to get, like those horseshoes."

Clover wondered where he was going with this, but she kept quiet as he continued.

"I know it's difficult being patient," Dad said, "but if you try, the minute you have enough money to get whatever it is you're wanting, I will bring you back to the store."

"Promise?" she asked.

"I promise."

7

MOM'S OFFER

When Clover and Dad returned with empty saddle-bags, Mom was proud of her daughter.

"You decided to save your money!" she said, smiling.

Clover looked at her without saying a word and trotted off to be alone in her stall. She overheard Mom ask Dad what had happened.

"She saw all sorts of new and exciting things at the store," Clover heard Dad say, "but she couldn't afford any of them with just $10. She's feeling a bit disappointed."

A moment later, Clover heard Mom at the door to her stall.

"Clover, may I come in?" Mom asked softly.

"I guess," she answered blandly, wiping the tears from her cheeks.

Mom walked in and sat next to her. "Dad and I don't like seeing you sad, sweetie. We aren't doing this to upset you. But you're old enough now to understand the value of saving your money."

Clover didn't move or say a word. She was still disappointed with the day's outcome, feeling rather grumpy by this point.

"What if . . ." Mom started to say. Then she shook her head. "Nah. You wouldn't want to do that." She glanced sideways at Clover and saw she had gotten her daughter's attention.

"What?" Clover asked, curiosity not allowing her to keep silent any longer.

"Well . . . what if tomorrow morning we went to the bank and opened your very own savings account? If you deposit your $10, Dad and I will also deposit $10, and then you'll have $20!"

Clover sat up straighter. "Really? Then I could go get the feather clip I really want!"

"Well now, wait one minute, Clover. You can't take all the money out of your account or else the bank will close it."

"Oh," Clover said, drooping her shoulders again.

"But if you wait one more week, you would have enough to get your feather clip *and* keep your account open."

Clover thought this over. It would be an easy extra $10 that she wouldn't have to do any chores for. And the feather clip definitely sounded more exciting than another bottle of glitter paint.

"Well, okay. I *guess* we could try that."

Mom smiled approvingly. "Maybe after we open your account, we could even go by The Feed Bucket for lunch."

Another $10 *and* lunch? Now Clover couldn't wait for tomorrow to get here.

8

THE GOLDEN SADDLEBAGS BANK

Applejack

Clover was so excited about the day's events that she woke up at 7 a.m., ready to go to the bank. Mom had to tell her they weren't open yet, which made Clover a bit disappointed. More waiting. More patience. She could hardly stand the wait as she went about getting herself ready for the day.

When she finished brushing her teeth and mane, she went outside to play for a bit. When that got old, she ran a few laps in the arena. And when she got bored of that, she went back into the barn to find Mom.

"How much longer?"

Mom checked the clock. "It's 9 a.m. The bank should be open now."

"Yes!" Clover leapt in the air and kicked her back legs out in excitement. "Can we go right now?"

"Yep," Mom answered. "Go get your money while I get the paperwork we'll need."

Clover was confused. "What paperwork?"

"The bank will need to properly identify you before opening your account. They want to make sure you really are who you say you are."

"But can't you tell them that I am telling the truth?"

Mom chuckled softly. "I wish it were that easy, but if it were, it would also be easy for anyone to come in and take your money."

Clover's eyes widened. "I don't want someone taking my money! I work hard for my allowance."

Mom nodded. "Exactly. That's why the bank will want to see your birth certificate and social security card to open your account. They want to protect you."

"Will I have to bring those every time I go to the bank?" Clover asked.

"No, only to open your account. After that, they usually ask grown-ups to see their IDs. But for kids, they ask a couple identifying questions, like where you were born, your birthday, or a special password that you can choose. And if they get to know you personally, they won't need to see or ask you anything."

After thinking about this for a minute, Clover felt she understood the process. She cantered back to her stall, put her $10 bill into her saddlebags, and joined Mom to trot to the bank. If it were up to Clover, they would have galloped the whole way there, but Mom kept using that dreaded word: *patience*.

At last, she saw the bank come in to view and read the sign: Golden Saddlebags Bank. Walking inside, the teller smiled as they approached his window.

"Good morning, Mrs. Triplecrown! How can I help you today?"

Clover waited for Mom to answer, but instead Mom looked down at Clover and said, "Go ahead, sweetie. Tell Applejack why we're here."

Clover was stunned. Mom was letting her be in charge? She felt like a grown-up as she stood up nice and tall, and said, "I want to open a savings account, please."

"Wow, your very own savings account?" Applejack asked. Clover nodded proudly as he added, "That's quite a big deal! Let me find someone who can help you."

The teller asked them to follow him over to a desk with a sign that read New Accounts.

He told the mare sitting there, "This young filly wants to open her very own savings account with us. Can you help her, River?"

"Absolutely!" she answered. "I'd be glad to."

The teller gave Clover a wink and walked back to his station. River, the mare handling new accounts, turned her attention to Clover.

"What a big step you're taking," she said. "Saving your money is a smart thing to do."

"I know," Clover said. She ignored Mom's soft chuckle next to her, pretending that opening a bank account had been her own idea all along.

9

CLOVER'S VERY OWN BANK ACCOUNT

"Did you bring in your birth certificate and social security card for me?" River asked.

Clover nodded, got them out of Mom's saddlebags, and passed them across the desk to River.

River read them and then began asking Clover a few questions as she worked on her computer. "What's your name, little filly?"

"Clover Triplecrown!" she said boldly.

"What a beautiful name. And when is your birthday?"

"October 6, 2019."

"Oh, someone just had a birthday," River said with her eyes wide.

Clover nodded. "Yes! Me! I just turned seven."

River smiled and winked at Clover. "Well, happy birthday!"

River gathered the rest of the information she needed, including some things from Mom. She would be a joint owner on Clover's account to help guide her as she learned all about how it worked, but the money and the decisions were all Clover's.

A few minutes later, River started printing up some documents. Setting them in front of Clover, she motioned to the bottom of the form.

"You will need to sign and date for me, and then we will be ready to make your very first deposit!"

"Wow, that was fast," Clover said.

"Pretty painless, huh?" River said jokingly.

Feeling very mature, Clover picked up the pen with her mouth and signed her name as fancily as she could at the bottom of the form, adding lots of curls and twirls. Mom signed below her and then passed the paperwork back to River, who then pushed a small blue book across the desk toward Clover.

"This is your new deposit book. Each time you make a deposit or take out a withdrawal, your teller will write it down in here. That way, you will always know how much money you have in your account."

Clover looked at it. It was blank for now, but that would soon change.

"How much will you be opening your account with today, Clover?"

"$20," she answered.

River nodded and filled out the deposit slip. "Would you like to come with me to make the deposit?"

Clover nodded excitedly and followed River back over to the nice teller named Applejack.

"Congratulations!" he said, taking the deposit slip from River.

"Thank you." Clover smiled brightly and handed him her two $10 bills and her deposit book.

Applejack worked at his computer for a couple of seconds, put the cash in his drawer, filled out Clover's deposit book, and then handed it back to her. "Here you go, Clover!"

"Thank you," she said, turning to follow River back over to her desk.

"Ready to go?" Mom asked Clover when they returned.

"One more thing," River interrupted. She pulled out a box from her drawer and pushed it toward Clover. "You can pick any of these stickers to put on the front of your deposit book."

Clover felt like she was getting all sorts of new and exciting things today. Why hadn't she done this sooner? She browsed the stickers and ended up choosing one that read, "I Have Horse Cents!" It had a saddle-shaped piggie bank and a coin hanging over it as though it were about to be dropped in.

"Oh, great choice!" River said. "That one is my favorite. Don't forget to sign your name inside the front cover just as pretty as you did on your signature card."

"Okay." Clover beamed. She took the paper backing off her new sticker, applied it carefully to the cover of her blue book, and then flipped to the inside cover to sign her name for a second time that day.

When Clover finished, River said, "Welcome to the Golden Saddlebags Bank family, Miss Clover!"

Clover beamed at her. "Thank you!"

Mom thanked River before turning to Clover. "Okay, ready for lunch now?"

"Ready!"

10

DECISIONS, DECISIONS . . .

A week later, Mom handed Clover her allowance again, and Dad reminded her she now had enough money for the feather clip she wanted. At first, Clover was excited about the idea of going back to Mane

Attraction to get it, but then she thought about the imprint horseshoes.

"Actually, I think I'll wait a bit longer," she told him.

"Wow, Clover," Mom said. "You're being so patient."

For the next several weeks, when Clover got her allowance, she would beg to go straight to the bank to make her deposit. River and Applejack greeted her by name every time she walked into the Golden Saddlebags Bank, which made Clover feel really important. Applejack also let her pick out a sticker each time. She loved having her own bank account!

When five long weeks of eager anticipation had finally passed, Clover had saved up enough money for the glittery imprint horseshoes she'd been dreaming of. She was so excited to finally buy them that she reared up with glee the moment Dad got home from hauling in grain for the winter months.

"Daddy! Can you take me to Mane Attraction today?"

"Sure thing," he said, sensing her joy. "Let me just put these grain buckets away."

Once he was done, they cantered together over to the bank. Clover would need to make her first withdrawal so she could use her money to buy the horseshoes.

"Hi, Clover!" Applejack said when he saw her. "What can I help you with today? Do you have another deposit to make?"

Clover shook her head. "Actually, I need to make a withdrawal, please."

"Ah," Applejack said, pulling out a withdrawal slip. "Your current balance is $60 and 60 cents. How much would you like to withdraw today?"

Clover's eyes widened. It was more than she was expecting. She didn't remember depositing the 60 cents.

Applejack could see her confusion and he answered her unspoken question, "You earn interest with a savings account. So, however much money is in your account, the bank adds a percentage to it each month."

"Wow!" Clover was excited about this. She could earn money without doing anything except having her allowance money in her savings account.

"Pretty cool, huh?" Applejack said. "So, how much would you like to withdraw today?"

Clover did some quick math. The horseshoes were $15 each. Four of them would be $60. She already had $10 from her allowance she received today, so she needed $50 more. "$50, please."

Applejack filled out the slip, did some work on his computer, marked the interest earned and the withdrawal in Clover's passbook, and then handed her a crisp $50 bill. "Here you go, little lady. Spend it wisely."

"I will," Clover said. "See you next week!"

She turned and darted out the door, Dad trotting after her.

At long last, Clover and Dad arrived at Mane Attraction. Clover burst through the door ahead of Dad and went straight to the horseshoes. When Dad caught up to her, he watched as she shuffled them around to see all of her options.

"Which ones will you choose?" he asked.

"I like them all!" Clover exclaimed. Now that she was finally able to buy them, she was having a hard time deciding which she liked best. Pink was her favorite color, but she also liked teal. And she couldn't decide between the dragonfly and the clover imprints.

"Well, you don't have to get all the same kind. You could get four different ones."

Clover loved this idea. "Like a rainbow!" she said.

"Exactly," Dad said with a nod.

Clover started picking them up one by one, tossing four different colored horseshoes with four different imprints into her saddlebags. She chose a pink one with dragonfly imprints, a teal one with clovers, a purple one with hearts, and a blue one with butterflies.

With her saddlebags heavy from the horseshoes, Clover pranced over to the cashier and very proudly placed them onto the counter in front of her.

11

CLOVER'S PATIENCE
PAYS OFF

Clover was so excited she was prancing in place in front of the cashier, whose name tag read, Willow.

"Ah, great choices," Willow said. "And you came on the perfect day! These imprint horseshoes are on sale this week—buy three, get one free."

"What a great deal," Dad said.

Clover's face lit up with joy. "Really?"

"Yep!" Willow answered. "That'll be $45, please."

Clover happily passed the crisp $50 bill she'd just gotten from Applejack at the bank across the counter to Willow, who gave her $5 back. Clover put that along with her $10 bill from her allowance this week back into her saddlebags. She did not expect to have money left over after buying her new horseshoes, so this was pretty exciting. She could go deposit this extra $15 right back into her account!

"Your patience really paid off, Clover," Dad said. "Do you want to look around for something else to buy with your extra money? Maybe one of those feather clips?"

Clover thought about it for a moment. She did really like that feather clip she saw last time she was here, but she didn't want to be too hasty and make a decision she'd regret. There were other things she wanted also, like that fancy teal grooming bag she'd spotted on the way to the horseshoes today. She could use it to carry all of her brushes and ribbons. It cost $25, so she didn't have enough left to get it today, but if she saved up just $10 more, she could get it as soon as next week.

Now that Clover knew the power of saving her money, she understood that instead of getting something she sort of wanted right now, it was way more exciting and gratifying to save up and get something she really wanted, even though it took a lot of patience.

Mom had been right. Clover was proud of herself for what she had accomplished. She'd managed to save up her money, be very patient, and buy the sparkly imprint horseshoes all by herself. Maybe she'd even start saving up her bonus stars for a trip to Cross-Country Jumps Theme Park. That would be a whole day of fun!

After some serious thought, Clover decided she should keep the $15 she had saved today until she was certain about what she wanted to do with it. And who knew? Maybe someday she'd even have enough for that beautiful saddle with the sunflower tooling!

Mind made up, Clover looked up at Dad and smiled.

"No thanks, Dad. I think I'll put it back in my savings account and save up for a while."

The End

THANK YOU, READER!

Thank You for Reading My Book!

Every author knows that each of their readers is extremely valuable. Word of mouth is truly what makes a book hit the best-seller list.

So . . .

Can You Help Spread the Word?

Reviews are incredibly important for authors—they are worth their weight in gold. Please be sure to leave me an honest review wherever you bought this book.

And if you know a parent, school, or even a bank who might enjoy this book, please be sure to tell them about it!

ACKNOWLEDGMENTS

To My Husband:

Thank you for your incredible patience as I worked overtime to finally get this book published. You spent your own downtime reading the final draft and offering me feedback, and you encouraged me to see it through to publication. You really are my best friend, forever and for always.

To My Daughters:

Ember and Karissa, you were my inspiration behind this book being written over six years ago and finally coming to fruition today. Thank you for being my very special beta readers. You were the first ever to listen to any of my original stories (many that I wrote just for you), and your love and excitement to hear each of them helped encourage me to finally finish this book.

To My Parents:

Thank you for always believing in me. Even as a young child, you supported and encouraged my love of the written word, which ignited a wildfire within me!

Thank you also for teaching me the value of saving my money—a powerful lesson that I still remember clearly so many years later.

To My Mother-in-Law:

You have always been so supportive of my book editing business, regularly purchasing my clients' books to read or gift to others. I already know without asking that you will do the same with my own book, and for that, I am truly grateful.

To My Colleague and Friend Rachel:

You are like my personal cheerleader at times, and I so appreciate you. Thank you for reading over my manuscript and giving your feedback, and thank you for giving it one final quick read when I made some last-minute changes.

To My Colleague and Friend Nikki of Jot & Tittle: A Proofreading Service:

Thank you for checking this manuscript over for those pesky lingering errors. Even editors need editors, and I am grateful to have you in both my network and my corner.

To My Client and Friend Tracy:

Working with you as my editing client and seeing your natural artistic talent in your own books made me excited to become *your* client and watch my own characters come to life. Thank you for agreeing to illustrate *Horse Cents* for me and for the passion you brought into making Clover's personality shine through.

ABOUT THE AUTHOR

Mandi currently lives in Northern California with plans to move to coastal Oregon this year. She lives with her best friend and husband, Lane, and her two wonderful daughters, Ember (six) and Karissa (three). Her family loves living in the rural country-side with their dog, Bo, and horses, Kaylee and Blue.

Devoted to instilling the love of books within her daughters, Mandi makes sure to read to them every single day and is excited to share *Horse Cents* with them as well. Mandi is also passionate about pet adoption and enjoys camping with her family, riding the trails with her horses, and reading on the beach with the waves crashing rhythmically in the background. Her all-time favorite book is *A Connecticut Yankee in King Arthur's Court* by Mark Twain.

With a passion for the written word, Mandi loves all things books and has written creatively since she was a child. She wrote countless short stories and had a poem published in a collection after winning a contest at the young age of eleven. As an adult, Mandi received her bachelor's degree with honors in English with a concentration in creative writing. With this foundation, it made perfect sense when she began dreaming of breaking into the field of book editing.

Mandi launched Red Quill Co LLC in 2020 and enjoys everything about it: meeting new people from all over the world, editing a variety of topics and genres, and helping her clients improve their manuscripts to become the best possible books they can be. Check out her website at www.RedQuillCo.com to learn more about Mandi, subscribe to her newsletter, or check out her editing services to see how she could help you with your book!

DISCUSSION QUESTIONS

About Clover

1. How do you think Clover felt when she couldn't get what she wanted right away? Do you think it was fair that she had to wait? Why or why not?
2. How do you think Clover felt when she opened her very own bank account? How about when she managed to save up enough money to buy her sparkly horseshoes?
3. Why do you think Clover decided to save the money at the end of the book instead of getting something else in addition to her new horseshoes?
4. Do you think Clover will ever get the saddle with the sunflower tooling? Why or why not?

About You

1. Do you earn an allowance? What chores do you have to do to earn it? How does it make you feel?
2. What do you do with your allowance when you earn it?
3. Do you find it difficult to save your money instead of buying something right away?
4. Do you have a savings account? Would you want to open one of your very own?

A GLOSSARY OF BANKING TERMS

Account

Your account is identified by a 10- to 12-digit number and is held in your name. This is how the bank's computer system keeps track of your balance and transactions.

ACH

An acronym that stands for Automated Clearing House. This is an electronic transaction such as when your parents pay their bills online, make a purchase online with their checking account information, or receive their paycheck directly into their account.

ATM

ATM

An acronym that stands for Automated Teller Machine. This is a computer-like machine that contains account information and paper bills. It allows a customer access to their bank account 24/7 even during non-banking hours by using an ATM card or debit card and PIN number to identify yourself. It pulls up your account information and you can then deposit or withdraw funds from your account or simply check your balance.

ATM Card

Similar in appearance to a credit card, this card is linked to a savings account and can only be used at the ATM. It does not have a major credit card logo (such as Visa or MasterCard) and cannot be used to make a purchase in a store.

Balance

The amount of money you have in your bank account.

Bank

The entity that keeps track of and secures the money in your bank account.

Banking Days / Hours

Bank

The time that your bank is open. Usually Monday through Friday from 8 or 9 a.m. until 5 p.m.

Birth Certificate

A government-issued document that has all the information about your birth including the date, time, location, and your parents' names and information.

CD

An acronym for Certificate of Deposit. This is similar to a savings account in that the point is to save your money and you earn interest. The big difference is that you can't withdraw the money until the CD matures, meaning it has fulfilled the term, or amount of time, that you chose when opening it. That time-frame can vary anywhere from a few months to several years.

Checking Account

An account that can have a debit card and checks linked to it, but does not earn interest. This is the type of account most grown-ups use to pay the bills.

Checks

Checks

A piece of paper with your name, address, bank name and bank address, account number, and bank routing number. There are also blank lines for you to fill out including the date, the payee (the person or company you are paying), and the amount you wish to pay (both numerical and written forms are required), and a place for you to sign your name. When the payee cashes or deposits the check, the amount is deducted from your checking account. Checks often come in "books" of several checks stuck together like in a notebook.

Credit

A transaction that adds to your account balance such as a deposit.

Debit

A transaction that subtracts from your account balance, such as a withdrawal.

Debit Cards

Debit Cards

Similar to a credit card in appearance and function, this card is linked to a checking account and sometimes a savings account as well. It will have a logo from one of the major credit card companies (such as Visa or MasterCard) and can be used at the ATM or to make a purchase in a store. If you make a purchase, the amount will be deducted from your checking account.

Deposit

Anytime you add money to your account, you are making a deposit or a credit. That amount is added to your total balance.

EFT

An acronym for Electronic Funds Transfer. This is a transfer of funds between two accounts, including a withdrawal or debit from one account and the matching deposit or credit into another account.

ID

Also called an identification card, this is a government-issued document the shape and size of a credit card that has your picture and identifying information on it, including your hair color, eye color, date of birth, address, height, weight, and gender. Grown-ups usually carry their IDs with them in their wallet and use them to verify their identity when using a credit card or at a bank.

Interest

Some types of accounts earn interest, which is based on a percentage of your account balance. This means that simply by having money in your account, the bank will add some money to it as well. The interest is earned daily and usually deposited once a month.

Joint Account

Interest

When two or more people share an account. An account with a child on it will require an adult to be on the account as well to help guide them as they learn how to manage their money.

Mint

The government entity that creates the money used in your country. In the US, this would be the US Mint, which makes our dollar bills and coins.

New Accounts

The department at the bank that helps you open a new account. They are knowledgable in the types of accounts and services the bank offers and can help you decide what type of account is right for you.

Online Banking

An account created on your bank's website that allows you to log in and check your balance. If you have more than one account, you can also initiate transfers between them. If you

Paper Bills

have a checking account, you can use this service to pay bills as well.

Paper Bills

The paper money made by your government's mint. In the US, this would be the US dollar made by the US Mint.

Passbook

A small pocket-sized book, usually blue, that allows you to keep track of your deposits and withdrawals from your savings account so you always know your balance.

Passbook

PIN

An acronym for Personal Identification Number. It is a 4-digit number of your choosing that allows you to use your debit card at the ATM or in a store.

POS

An acronym for Point of Sale. This is when you use your debit card at a store like you would a credit card. If you choose to sign instead of entering your PIN, you would be running it as credit, and the transaction would be coded as a POS.

Savings Account

This account is intended to encourage you to save your money using incentives like earned interest and a limited number of withdrawals allowed per quarter.

Social Security Card

A government-issued document the shape and size of a credit card, only it is made from paper rather than plastic. It contains your social security number.

Social Security Number

This is a 9-digit number linked only to you out of everyone in the whole world. It should be protected and kept in a secure location in your home.

Teller

A person who works at the bank and helps you make deposits, withdrawals, and check your balance.

Transactions

The deposits and withdrawals made using your bank account.

Transaction Register

Similar to a passbook, this is used to keep track of your transactions involving your checking account so you always know your balance.

Transaction Register

Withdrawal

Anytime you take money out of your account, you are making a withdrawal or a debit. That amount is deducted from your total balance.

A GLOSSARY OF HORSE TERMS

Alfalfa

A plant that is sometimes mixed into hay bales and fed to horses, but is high in calories (it's the horse-equivalent of eating cake).

Arena

A rectangular fenced-in area with dirt or sand for the ground where horses and riders exercise or compete.

Bale of Hay

Bale

A rectangular or round grouping of hay that is bound together with twine or wire.

Barrel Racing

Competitive horseback riding in which horse and rider race around three barrels in a specific pattern and back to the start as quickly as possible.

Barrel Racing

Bay

A horse that is brown in color, whether light or dark.

Bit

A piece of metal that attaches to the bridle and goes in the horse's mouth.

Blaze

A wide white stripe down a horse's face.

Bit

Bridle

The headgear, usually made of leather, with which a horse is guided or directed while being ridden.

Bronco

A horse that is not tamed or trained yet (also called a bronc).

Bronc Riding

A rodeo competition in which a rider gets on a bareback bronc and tries to stay on for at least eight seconds.

Bridle

Buck

When a horse kicks out their back legs; it can indicate playfulness, fear, or anger.

Buckskin

A horse that is grayish yellow in color.

Canter

The English term for a horse's running pace.

Bucking Bronco

Chestnut

A horse that is a reddish brown in color.

Colt

A young male horse.

Cross-Country

Competitive English-style horseback riding on a trail course in which horse and rider display their skills with endurance and style over jumps and obstacles.

English Saddle

Curry Comb

A circular-shaped brush with rubber or metal teeth used to get loose fur and any debris out of a horse's coat.

Dressage

Competitive English-style horseback riding in a large arena in which horse and rider display their graceful skills at each of the gaits.

English Riding

The style of riding typically used in dressage, show jumping, and cross-country.

Foal

Filly

A young female horse.

Foal

A gender-neutral term for a baby horse.

Gait

A horse's pace, whether the walk, trot/jog, canter/lope, or gallop.

Gallop

Gallop

The universal term for a horse's sprinting pace.

Gelding

A neutered male horse.

Gray

A horse that is white or gray in color.

Grooming

The action of brushing a **horse** and picking their hooves.

Grooming Bucket

A bucket that carries all the grooming supplies.

Halter

The headgear, usually made of nylon or rope, that goes on a horse's head and attaches to a lead rope to allow a person to lead a horse around from the ground.

Halter with Lead Rope

Hands

The measurement used to tell how tall a horse is at the withers. Each hand is equal to about four inches.

Hay

Grass that is grown, cut, and baled for feeding to horses or other livestock.

Herd

A group of horses. It is also the action of moving horses from one location to another.

Hoof

The foot of a horse made of keratin (the same stuff our fingernails are made of).

Herd of Horses

Hoofpick

A pick used to clean dirt and rocks out of the bottom of a horse's hooves.

Horseshoe

A curved piece of metal that is connected by a special type of nail to the bottom of a horse's hoof.

Jog

The western term for a horse's jogging pace.

Horseshoes

Lead Rope

A rope that attaches to a halter to lead a horse around from the ground.

Lope

The western term for a horse's running pace.

Mane

The hair that grows along a horse's neck.

Mare

A female horse.

Paint Horse

Palomino

A horse that is a pale cream or golden color, usually paired with a flaxen mane and tail.

Paint

A horse that is marked with patches of white and another color such as black, brown, or even palomino.

Prance

A fancy gait when horses use high springing steps.

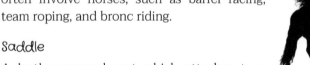

Rear

When a horse rises up to stand on only its two back legs, lifting its front legs into the air.

Reins

A strap usually made of leather that is connected to the bit and bridle to communicate to a horse while riding.

Rodeo

A variety of western-style competitions that often involve horses, such as barrel racing, team roping, and bronc riding.

Saddle

A leather-covered seat which attaches to a horse's back for the rider to sit on.

Saddlebags

Bags that attach to the front or back of a saddle for the purpose of carrying items (similar to a backpack).

Show Jumping

An English-style competition that takes place in a large arena in which the horse and rider display their skills at gracefully jumping over a variety of jumps and obstacles.

Star

A small white spot on the upper part of a horse's face.

Stallion

An unneutered male horse.

Stirrup

The pieces of the saddle that the rider puts their feet in. These are often called irons in English-style riding.

Tack

The gear used to ride a horse, such as a saddle and bridle.

English & Western Stirrup

Team Roping

A western-style competition in which a pair of horses and riders team up to rope a calf (baby cow) in the shortest amount of time.

Tooling

Detailed artwork that is carved into leather, such as on a saddle or bridle.

Trot

The English term for a horse's jogging pace.

Western Riding

The style of riding typically used in ranching and rodeos.

Western Saddle with Tooling

Withers

A horse's shoulder bone at the base of its neck. This is the point used to measure a horse's height.

CPSIA information can be obtained
at www.ICGtesting.com
Printed in the USA
BVHW052035200223
658864BV00010B/191